**This book is dedicated to those special people of Tibet
who live among the highest mountains in the world. My
earnest desire is that they might come to know
the King of Heaven.**

Douglas Blackwood
4th. August 1986

DAWA BEMA
THE UNCERTAIN MONK
by Douglas Blackwood
Photos by Douglas Blackwood

© Copyright 1987 by Scandinavia
Publishing House, Nørregade 32, DK-1165 Copenhagen K.
English-language edition first published 1988
through special arrangement with Scandinavia
jointly by Wm.B. Eerdmans Publishing Co.,
255 Jefferson Ave. S.E., Grand Rapids, Michigan 49503

Printed in Hong Kong

ISBN 0-8028-5023-5

DAWA BEMA
The Uncertain Monk

Douglas Blackwood

Photos by Douglas Blackwood

William B. Eerdmans Publishing Company
Grand Rapids, Michigan

Dawa Bema loved the wild mountains which rose up all around him to meet the clouds. He herded his sheep farther up the rocky slopes, looking for scattered bits of grass. A huge wall of ice, or glacier, rose from the highest part of the mountain. It was icy-blue. Streams of clear water rushed from rock to rock, splashing and spilling in all the different colors of the rainbow. Spring was coming, Dawa Bema could tell, because millions of tiny wild flowers had turned the mountain gold.

The shepherd boy stretched and looked down at his flock of sheep. The warm sun felt good on his face. He had been thinking about how he would soon have to leave his mountains, and never come back. He was not happy about it. But ever since Dawa Bema was a little boy, his parents had told him he would be a monk. And this meant that soon he must leave home and start studying. Dawa Bema (his name meant "The Moon") would be ten years old in a few weeks. After his birthday he would have to go and live in a **gompa**, the monastery for Tibetan monks. Not only must he leave his flocks, but he could never have a normal life, marry, or be a father.

The boy was the third son in his family. And according to Tibetan tradition, which had not changed very much in the past thousand years, the third son was supposed to become a monk. The day he was born, Dawa Bema's father, mother, and grandparents had agreed. Nothing could change their minds.

Dawa Bema nervously twisted the leather strip on his sling. The woven straps looped together in a pouch, just the right size for a stone. He dreamed of taking his sheep to a distant valley, far away from all the thoughts of gompa and monks. But he knew Lamaism, the Tibetan religion, was the most important thing to all his people living in Tibet, and there was no place where it could not reach him. Tibet had been closed for centuries to people from other countries. He had never met anyone from outside his world of mountains. There was nowhere else.

Suddenly, Dawa Bema sat up stiffly. What was that he saw?

The sheep huddled together in fear. Dawa Bema listened, but heard nothing. His eyes searched the pasture. Then he saw them, almost invisible next to the big rocks. There stood two fierce wolves. They had been following the flock of sheep.

Dawa Bema held his breath. He carefully climbed the rocky slope, pretending not to see the wolves. They were about to attack the terrified sheep and did not see him bend down to pick up a rock for his sling. He spun the sling over his head, faster and faster, until it was humming through the air. Then, at just the right moment, he let go one leather strap and the stone whistled downward. It was a perfect shot! One of the wolves crumpled to the ground. The other wolf ran off in fright. Dawa Bema yelped with excitement.

The sling was Dawa Bema's favorite thing in the whole world. He always carried it with him. In the past, his tribe had always had to protect themselves against wild animals, bandits, and the Khampa horsemen. The Khampas had been worse than the wild animals. Dawa Bema's grandfather sometimes told him stories about how he had once fought off a band of Khampas single-handedly.

For hundreds of years, his tribe had herded sheep and yaks, the long-haired cows of Tibet, on the icy mountain slopes. When it was warm enough, they had planted crops and the yaks had pulled the plows. Each year Dawa Bema collected yak manure. That was made into a type of brick that could be burned. There were no trees for wood.

The winters were so cold that meat froze and could be kept outside. Snowstorms blew for weeks and made life very hard. Dawa Bema did not like the winters. All he could do then was sit inside by the stove and try to stay warm.

Dawa Bema rounded up his sheep. He checked the slope quickly to make sure the wolf had not come back. Then he set off down the mountain. His village was far below, next to the river.

Prayer flags blew in the wind. Every mud-brick house had one on its roof. Dawa Bema's dog, Nyima (the name meant "sun"), ran out to jump up on Dawa Bema. He wagged his tail and started barking — he was so happy to see his master.

Dawa Bema stepped through the gateway and into a small yard next to his house. Mother was busy cooking and Father was sifting flour.

"I killed a wolf with my sling," Dawa Bema said proudly. "It only took one shot!"

His parents looked up and smiled. "Well done, well done," his father said.

Dawa Bema looked at his brother, Lobsang Samten, but he had nothing to say.

Lobsang Samten was Dawa Bema's older brother. He was jealous that Dawa Bema got to wander the mountain with his sheep while he always had to stay home. The two boys often argued about who was the stronger and faster.

There had been an eldest brother, but he had died from typhoid, a bad fever caused by drinking dirty water.

Once, Lobsang Samten had also been very sick. There had been no doctor in the village. His mother had placed snow on his forehead to keep him from getting too hot.

Father had been afraid the fever was a curse on his family, so he had built a little place for prayer in the house. Dawa Bema had had to keep the candles burning. Day and night for a month, he made sure there was enough yak butter in the candle pots so the fire would not go out. Then, when Lobsang Samten got better, Father thought it was because Dawa Bema had prayed so much to Buddha, the god worshipped by people in Tibet.

The brothers went inside. The dark room, which the family also slept in, was full of odd bits of furniture and a radio, the family's favorite possession.

"**Om mani padme hum. Om mani padme hum**," Dawa Bema said over and over again. He knelt in the corner for prayer. The words he had said were very, very old. They were a **mantra**, or prayer to the Buddha. On the wall hung pictures of the Buddha and several lamas. Dawa Bema had been brought up to believe the Buddha was a god. The lamas were living buddhas.

The first Buddha, Sakyamuni, who had lived 2,400 years ago, taught life was like a wheel, or **Dharma**, which never stopped turning. Each time a person died, his soul returned in the form of another person. A Tibetan hoped that someday he would not have to be reborn every time he died. Before that could happen, though, he had to live a perfect life. That would mean he had reached a place called **Nirvana**. Nirvana was a type of heaven. It was not really a place though, more a way of thinking. And that is what every monk worked toward.

Dawa Bema prayed to the Buddha to help him work hard at becoming a monk. All the same, he was not even sure he wanted to be a monk.

Lobsang Samten watched his brother closely. He could tell something was bothering Dawa Bema.

"I don't even think I want to be a monk," Dawa Bema said suddenly. He stood up and walked out of the door into the sunshine. "My home is here!"

"Don't you dream of going to Lhasa?" asked Lobsang Samten, joining him outside. "I've heard fantastic stories of how every roof there is covered with gold. And the city walls touch the sky."

Dawa Bema had heard the stories too. Lhasa, the holy city of Tibet, once forbidden to outsiders, was a sparkling fairy tale city. It was where the **Dalai Lama**, or king of all the lamas, had lived until he escaped to India when the Chinese army invaded Tibet.

Dawa Bema looked up at the sun, squinting. "I just don't know what I want," he said.

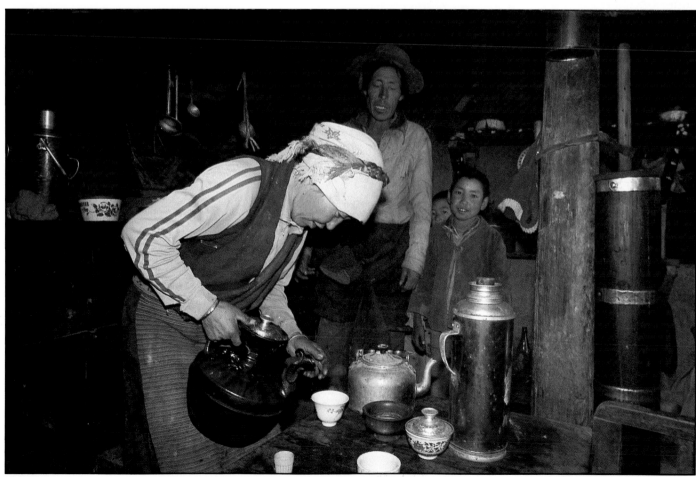

Suddenly several children ran along the alley shouting, "Dawa Bema! Dawa Bema! You have a visitor!"

Dawa Bema ran as fast as he could to the door and almost ran right into a young woman who had just been coming into the house.

"**Tashi dele**," she said. That was a way of saying "Hello" in Tibet and wishing all the best for the people whose home you were entering. "Are you Dawa Bema?"

Dawa Bema could not answer. All he could do was stare at the visitor and her strange clothes.

"My name is Lha Dron," she explained. "You won't know me, but I am your cousin. I've come a long way to visit your family ... from another country."

Dawa Bema's parents came to see who had arrived. None of them had ever seen anyone from another country before. They were all so surprised. Then Mother invited the visitor inside and brewed a pot of tea mixed with yak butter and salt.

Lha Dron talked about things and places Dawa Bema never even knew were real. Her father had been Dawa Bema's uncle. When she was a baby, her family had escaped from Tibet. It was just after the Chinese army had invaded Tibet. Her parents had died crossing the Himalayas, which were the tallest mountains in the world. Lha Dron had been saved by other Tibetans and taken to India. In that new land, she had grown up with a new way of living.

Dawa Bema could hardly believe all the new ideas he was hearing. Was there really another world beyond the huge southern mountains? Not only that, but Lha Dron told them about another God, One who turned darkness into light. But who could be greater than the Buddha, Dawa Bema wondered.

Lha Dron was the first person he had met who believed differently than all the other people. He wondered if he could possibly be different someday, too. Did he dare to question and go against the way things had always been? He was not sure. It was strange that this visitor had come just as he was about to leave and become a monk.

13

Lha Dron stayed several days. Dawa Bema liked her, but was not too sure whether he believed all her stories.

After she left, all of Dawa Bema's family helped him get ready for the long trip to Lhasa, where he would learn to become a monk. They packed grain and yak butter, which the family would offer as gifts to the gompa. The barley grain would be cooked to make **tsampa**, a sticky, doughy meal when mixed with yak butter tea.

The day for Dawa Bema to leave finally came. The boy looked for his dog and found Nyima in a dark corner, curled up in a ball. The dog must have known that Dawa Bema was leaving. He had not moved for days. Nyima licked his master's face. Dawa Bema had wanted to take his dog with him, but it was not allowed.

Next he had to say good-bye to his family. Mother was crying. His little sister gave him a present made from yak hair. His friends were all waiting to see him off.

Dawa Bema wished he could say good-bye to every animal and special place he loved, but there just was not time. Quickly, he climbed the short ladder onto the roof of his house. From the top he looked across the village to the distant mountains. He took a deep breath and shouted the blessing that all would keep well, "Tashi dele!" He listened, and heard the mountains echo their farewell.

Lobsang Samten rode out with his brother and father as far as the first hill. Dawa Bema pulled out his sling and held it out to his brother. "I can't take it where I'm going," he said. He was afraid he would cry. "Take care of my sheep." Then he cracked the reins and his horse started to trot away. Dawa Bema looked straight ahead, but his heart wanted more than anything else to go back.

The first bumpy day passed slowly. Many more days were to follow. Dawa Bema thought about sharing his doubts with his father, but fear of what he might think kept Dawa Bema quiet.

By the seventh day of the trip, the road, which kept going up and up, seemed as though it would never end. Dawa Bema and his father had blisters on their feet. And the horses and donkeys were so tired that they had to be pushed over the last part of the last mountain. During the trip they had crossed three mountains, each well over five thousand meters high. That was so high that it was hard for Dawa Bema and his father to breathe. No matter what direction they turned, all they saw was an endless field of snow-capped mountain peaks.

After ten days, they had almost reached Lhasa. They saw more and more people on the road, the closer they got to the holy city. Many of them carried brightly-colored prayer flags. Even though Dawa Bema was dragging his feet from the long journey and already missed home, he was very excited about seeing his first city.

As they rounded a bend in the valley Dawa Bema's eyes suddenly lit up. "Is that it?" he gasped. "Is that the...?"

"The Potala!" his father shouted. They dropped to their knees, lifted their arms to the sky, and fell forward, flat on the ground. Around them, other pilgrims, or travellers, prayed in the same way.

"Om mani padme hum! Om mani padme hum!"

Before them stood the holy city of Lhasa. And rising above the city was the Potala, the former palace of the Dalai Lama. Its golden roofs shimmered in the midday sun. The high walls and steps were like none Dawa Bema had ever seen. In his small village, the mud-brick houses had stood no higher than one story.

"One day, Dawa Bema, you may live in the Potala!" his father said.

"The Po...tala!" Dawa Bema was so excited that he could hardly talk. "You mean when I'm a monk?"

"I just know you will be a great monk and make me very proud," his father sighed.

Dawa Bema thought he was in a dream. Lhasa was like another world.

Once they arrived, Dawa Bema and his father went to the very old Jokhang Temple to light candles and pray to the giant statue of the Buddha.

Dawa Bema followed the other pilgrims walking slowly around the temple. Everyone walked in one direction, toward the right. Many pilgrims lay face down on the street, praying with their hands outstretched. Beside the temple door stood two enormous golden drums which the pilgrims spun, again always to the right, toward the right. Inside the temple were hundreds of small, spinning drums. He saw some pilgrims carrying small prayer wheels which whirred when they spun. Each time someone finished walking around the temple, turning a drum or spinning a wheel, it was a prayer to the Buddha.

People had come from every part of Tibet to visit the temple. Some had travelled much farther than Dawa Bema. He saw many people with cracked and wrinkled faces and hands. The harsh sun and dry winds had left their mark.

Hundreds of monks gathered in the temple for the main prayers. Their dark red robes and bald heads made them stand out. Dawa Bema bowed every time a monk walked past him.

Father went inside the gompa, while Dawa Bema waited outside. As more people walked by him than he had ever seen before, he noticed they all smelled of yak butter. That was because they covered their hands and faces with the butter to protect their skin against the weather. Also, all the dark temples were lit by yak-butter candles, and it was the monks' job to make sure the candles did not go out.

Father came back after an hour. He was smiling. "You are accepted. We will go to see the Lama!"

Dawa Bema was not sure he could feel as excited as his father was.

An old monk led them through a gate and across a courtyard. A few monks looked up from their prayer books at Dawa Bema. They came to a dark hall. The walls were coated with black soot from the thousands of candles which had burned there during the many, many years.

A very thin man lit a candle and recited a prayer. This was the Lama. Dawa Bema was amazed. Here was a man who had almost reached Nirvana. Father told how they had brought three **poon goo**, or donkey-loads, of tsampa and yak butter. The Lama smiled and offered a second prayer. Father bowed. Then, without saying another word, he left the room.

Dawa Bema knew he could not follow. His heart sank into an empty hole in his stomach. He missed his father already.

"Today you have learned the first lesson of the monk," the Lama said softly. "Everything is behind you: your father, your life, all the things you think you want. Here you start a path which leads to the Buddha. Only if you forget all the rest can you ever walk this way. Do not think of your family anymore."

Dawa Bema stared at the flickering candles and nodded. For a Tibetan, there was supposed to be nothing better than to follow the Buddha.

During his first month Dawa Bema learned all about life in the gompa. His hair was cut off so he looked bald. He wore the brownish-red robe of a **rapjung**, or beginning monk. When he was 15 years old he would get to wear the red robes of a "**gestul**" monk. Then, when he became 20, he would become a **gelong**, or full monk. A gelong had to vow to follow 250 rules. Dawa Bema began by serving the other monks. Learning how to do what you were told was one of the first steps toward reaching Nirvana.

The gompa had hundreds of rooms, long halls, and stairways. Dawa Bema often got lost. Some rooms were pitch black. He discovered they were not necessarily empty, though, when one day he tripped over a monk who was praying in the dark. He was so scared that he ran until he was back outside again.

Sometimes the monks shouted at each other in a class about how to argue. Each monk had to learn how to defend what he believed. While they shouted, the monks would wave and clap their hands. Dawa Bema did not like this class. Once, when he was supposed to argue with an older monk, he became very mixed up.

Dawa Bema had to answer the question, "What is the purpose of a monk?" He thought about it and said, "The purpose of a monk is to do good."

"But the good is impossible to achieve," shouted back the older monk. "I say the monk's purpose is to escape from wanting to do anything, even if it is to do good!" And when he said the last word, the monk swung his right arm over his head and clapped his hands.

"But life is good...isn't it?" mumbled Dawa Bema meekly.

"No! Life is full of suffering. A monk seeks an escape!" He clapped again, on the word "escape."

Dawa Bema held his head in his hands and squirmed. "Yes, life is to escape....But to where?" he pleaded.

"To nowhere. No-where!" shouted the monk. The place they were all wanting to go, Nirvana, could not be described, except for calling it "no-thing" or "no-where."

The word "nowhere" rang through Dawa Bema's head again and again. He wanted to run and hide. But even the darkest rooms would not hide him.

Several times each day the monks would stop studying and praying in order to drink yak-butter tea. The tea was brewed in huge pots and brought out to the monks in big, shiny pitchers. All the youngest monks had to carry the heavy pitchers. And they had to be very careful not to spill any tea. That was bad luck. But it was even worse if the tea splashed into the cooking fire. The monks thought spirits lived in fire, wind, and water. If hot water spilled on the fire, the spirits would have been angry.

One day, while helping serve the tea, Dawa Bema met Tsering Gyurme, another young monk from a village close to Dawa Bema's. They soon found out they had herded yaks on different sides of the same mountain. Dawa Bema now had a friend who loved what he loved. Tsering Gyurme had been at the gompa for two years. He had learned that not all the monks were as bad as they seemed. Some even played hide-and-seek games in the gompa. Tsering Gyurme had often wanted to join in, but he didn't want to get caught. His head monk was very strict and never smiled.

Tsering Gyurme always carried his big tea pitcher with extra care. One time, though, when the cook was filling his pitcher, some boiling tea accidentally splashed onto his hand. He screamed and dropped his pitcher. Tea spilled across the floor, hissing and spitting as it reached the fire.

Dawa Bema heard the scream and ran to help. But another monk held him back. The head monk dragged Tsering Gyurme outside, in front of all the monks. He had to lie on the ground while each monk stepped on him. The head monk said this way the spirits would not be angry about the water in their fire.

Afterwards, Tsering Gyurme was so ashamed that he hid in a room and would not come out. Dawa Bema took him tsampa and tea. Every day he wished he and Tsering Gyurme could run away from the gompa. And even though he did not tell anyone how he felt, Dawa Bema was afraid the giant Buddha statue could read his mind.

He wished there was a god he could talk to, one who would help him not be afraid anymore.

As time went by, Dawa Bema often sat for hours alone. He only spoke about his feelings to a dog who reminded him of Nyima. He played with his prayer beads and kept thinking about his dream of going home. And sometimes he thought about Lha Dron and the faraway land beyond the high mountains.

One morning a monk told him a young woman was waiting to see him. He knew without a doubt it could only be Lha Dron. So he sneaked out to meet her.

"I want you to have this story," she said, giving him some rolled-up paper. "It's about a king who lived thousands of years ago in another land. Before he became a king, though, he was a shepherd boy."

Dawa Bema unrolled the paper. The story was handwritten in Tibetan. He had been learning how to read at the gompa. He read the words, "King David the Good Shepherd."

"The name David in Chinese is 'Dawei,'" interrupted Lha Dron, "just like your name." Dawa Bema stared at the name. "King David believed in one God," said Lha Dron, "a God who cares for us like a shepherd."

"A God like a shepherd!" exclaimed Dawa Bema, remembering the time he had fought off the wolves. He felt the tears coming.

"Do you miss being a shepherd?" asked Lha Dron.

One tear ran down Dawa Bema's face. He covered his face so she could not see how much he hurt inside.

"The God of King David loves you," said Lha Dron, gently. "He can be your shepherd."

Dawa Bema closed his eyes. A candle burned inside him. For the first time ever, he felt there might be hope.

Lha Dron told how she had come to know God as a shepherd while living in India with a Christian family. Dawa Bema remembered how, when he first met Lha Dron, he had only half-believed her stories. Now he believed everything she said. He was glad she was his cousin. Lha Dron then said she must go back to India.

So, early the next morning she set off on her long trip across the mountains.

Dawa

Bema sat alone in his room, his hand tightly clutching the paper he had been keeping hidden. Slowly he unrolled it again and, word by word, entered the story. Once, twice, then again and again he read every detail of David's life. He knew the story by heart, as well as any monk could have learned his prayers.

Now, whenever he prayed at the temple, Dawa Bema thought about the God of David rather than the Buddha. The statue no longer made him afraid. Finally, he made up his mind about what he must do.

When Dawa Bema went into the Lama's room, he held his breath. The old man sat on the floor praying. For half an hour Dawa Bema stood at attention. Suddenly the Lama looked up. "So you want to leave the gompa, the way to Nirvana?" he asked.

Dawa Bema was so surprised he could think of nothing to say. Dawa Bema had told no one he wanted to leave. He was sure the Lama must have read his mind. Then he found his voice. "I have to!" he said bravely.

"The way to Nirvana is narrow. Few find it. Go!" commanded the Lama, and he went back to his prayers. Dawa Bema stood still for a moment, not believing what he had heard. "**Tega**! Go!" the Lama shouted. The force of the word pushed Dawa Bema out of the room.

He ran to Tsering Gyurme's room. "I'm leaving the gompa!" he said. "Come with me!"

"I can't," said Tsering Gyurme. "My father would be too angry."

His answer tore Dawa Bema in two. He did not want to leave his friend behind, but he could not stand to stay in the gompa any longer either. He shoved the rolled-up paper with David's story on it into his friend's hand. "Read it," he said as he walked to the door. "One day you will join me on the mountain. Until then, tashi dele."

Tsering Gyurme sat alone. Through the window he saw Dawa Bema walk across the courtyard and out the gate.

Although Dawa Bema was free, he did not know which way to turn. He was now a **wanlog**, a monk who had given up. He was not sure what his family would do. Many families refused to take their sons back after they left the gompa.

Dawa Bema met some travellers headed in the same direction as his village, so he rode on. They saw his short hair, but said nothing. When they dropped Dawa Bema off, they made sure he had some food and water. He was still several days from home.

A chilly autumn breeze fell from the high mountains. Dawa Bema pulled his jacket up around his neck and walked down the road. He tried not to think about how unsure everything looked. If his family did not want him back again, he really did not know where he would go instead.

Suddenly, his foot tripped over something. He bent down and saw a piece of rope sticking out of the ground. He pulled it out and gave a shout. It was a sling! Quickly, he pulled off the lumps of dirt which clung to the rope. He tested the straps. They were strong, the sling was good. He plucked a smooth rock from the ground and pushed it into the sling's pouch. The stone whizzed as he swung it around his head. And as it whistled through the air Dawa Bema shouted. The sling was even better than his old one had been.

Dawa Bema searched for another rock. He laughed and danced in circles, holding the sling stretched above his head.

At the top of his voice, he shouted, "God of David, Good Shepherd, thank You, thank You."

The breeze bore his prayer along the valley floor. He ran and skipped. The colored mountains looked down and smiled. Dawa Bema, the shepherd, was at home again in his heart.

"How beautiful on the mountains are the feet of those who bring good news, who proclaim peace, who bring good tidings, who proclaim salvation, who say to Zion, 'Your God reigns!' "

Isaiah 52:7 NIV

Date Due

Code 4386-04, CLS-4, Broadman Supplies, Nashville, Tenn..
Printed in U.S.A.